# Max
## and the cat

Written by Nicola Moon

Illustrated by Kay Widdowson

Max was a little brown mouse.
Pecky was a big black crow.
One day Max went to the market to
find some food.

A cat went to the market too.
She went to find some food.

The cat saw Max.
'I will eat the little mouse,'
she said.

Max saw some cheese.

'I will eat the cheese,' he said.

Pecky was on the roof.

'Stop, Max! Stop!' she said.

'I can see a cat.'

But Max said,
'I can't see a cat.
And I want to eat the cheese.'

Max ran to get the cheese.
The cat ran to get Max.

'Oh, no,' said Pecky.

The cat will eat Max.

Pecky went down and down and down.

Pecky jumped on to a box and
the box fell on the cat.

The cat ran off.

'Now you can eat the cheese,'
said Pecky.
'And you can too,' said Max.
And they did.